Stop Thie

A Play

Written by Julia Donaldson

Illustrated by Diana Mayo

CHARACTERS

Yumi

Aki

Rika

The Judge

Taro

... and a **Narrator**

Scene 1

Narrator   *Rika the baker was selling her doughnuts in the market place.*

Rika   Doughnuts! Fresh doughnuts, going cheap! Only one yen each!

Taro	Four for me, please, Rika.
Yumi	And I'll have fourteen!
	Here's fourteen yen.
Rika	Fourteen! You'll burst, Yumi!
Yumi	I don't care if I do.

3

Rika	There's only one doughnut left.
	I'll eat it myself on my way home.
Aki	No, don't do that – give it to me.
	I'm starving!
Rika	Well... all right, then, Aki.
	That's one yen.
Aki	What? You're not going to charge me
	for your last doughnut, are you?

Rika   Perhaps I can afford to let you off.
I've done well today.
My basket is full of coins.

Taro   Take care on your way home.
I've heard there's a thief about.

Rika   I'll be careful. Goodbye!

Yumi   Wait! Here comes another customer!

Taro   It's the wise judge.

Judge   Good morning, Rika.

            A dozen doughnuts, please.

6

Rika   I'm sorry, Sir, they've all gone.
I'll save you a dozen for next week,
if you like.

Judge   Let's shake hands on that.

Aki   I wouldn't shake Rika's hand, Sir!

7

Judge   And why is that?

Aki   It's always so oily!

Rika   Well, what can you expect when I'm
handling oily doughnuts all day long?

Judge   I'd rather shake an oily hand that's
honest, than a clean one that's
dishonest!

Narrator   *Rika shook hands with the Judge.
Then she set off for home. After
a while she reached a hilltop
and yawned.*

Rika	I'll stop for a rest. But what about my basket? I know – I'll hide it in this bush!
Narrator	*When Rika woke up she looked in the bush, but her basket had gone. She ran back to the market place.*

Rika	Stop! There's a thief!
	Someone's stolen my basket!
Yumi	What, with all the coins in it?
Rika	Yes, the whole lot!
	What am I going to do?
Aki	Go home and make some more doughnuts!
Rika	I can't! I've no money to buy the flour or the oil or the sugar.
Taro	Dry your eyes, Rika. Here's the wise judge. He'll soon find the thief.
Judge	Back in town already, Rika? Have you brought me my doughnuts?
Rika	No, Sir. I've come to report a crime. Someone has stolen my basket of coins!

Yumi	Can you find the thief, Sir?
Taro	You're such a wise judge!
Judge	Perhaps. But first I must visit the scene of the crime.

Scene 2

Narrator *Rika led everyone to the hilltop.*

Rika Here we are, Sir. I put the basket in this bush, and then I went to sleep over here. When I woke up the basket had gone.

Judge	You put the basket in the bush,
	and when you woke up it had gone?
	In that case, Rika, the thief
	is right here!
Aki	What do you mean?
Judge	This bush is the thief!
	Bush, I arrest you!

Narrator	*They all started to laugh.*
Yumi	How can a bush be a thief?
Taro	Our wise judge is not so wise after all!
Aki	No – he's a complete idiot!
Judge	STOP! How dare you laugh? How dare you be rude to a judge? You will all go to prison!

Narrator *Everyone stopped laughing. They went down on their knees before the judge.*

Taro Sir, we are so very sorry!

Yumi Please don't send us to prison!

Aki Of course the bush is the thief!

Rika Please forgive them, Sir.

They really are sorry.

Judge   Very well, instead of going to prison you can all pay me three yen. You first, Yumi.

Yumi   Here you are, Sir. One, two, three!

Judge   Now it's your turn, Taro.

Taro   Certainly, O wise judge! Here you are. One, two, three!

Judge	Now you, Aki.
Aki	It's so unfair!
	I won't be able to feed my family.
	Here you are, then – one, two, three!
Judge	You are the thief, Aki. I arrest you!

Aki	What do you mean? You're mad! First you want to arrest a bush, then you blame a poor, honest woman like me.
Judge	A rich, dishonest woman, you mean. Empty your pockets, Aki.
Narrator	*Aki could not lie any longer. She emptied her pockets.*

Aki	Oh, all right, then, I admit it.
Rika	Look! All my coins!
Yumi	But how did you know that Aki had taken them, Sir?

Taro	Yes, tell us, O wise one!
Judge	The coins themselves told me.
Rika	What do you mean? Coins can't talk.
Judge	No, but coins can be oily –
	just as oily as your hands, Rika.

Rika   That's true – the coins people pay me do get oily in my hands.

Judge   And those three yen were still oily when Aki put them into *my* hand!

Yumi   You really are a wise judge, Sir!

Judge Well, Rika, what do you have to say?

Rika Thank you, Sir! You can have *two* dozen doughnuts next week. And you can have them for nothing!

One day, Peter's Mum was cleaning the living room when she happened to find an unusually large and revolting bogey.

"That's it!" she yelled. "I've had just about enough of this. If I find one more of these horrible things, there'll be no sweets for a month."

Peter decided to escape into the garden. He could feel something bogey-like up his nose and he wanted to investigate.

He sat down under the apple tree, had a quick look round to make sure no one was watching and began to pick away.

Then, still looking round, he stuck the bogey on the tree.

When Peter turned to look at the bogey, he couldn't believe his eyes. There on the tree was the biggest bogey he had ever seen. And it was moving!

"Wow!" he gasped. "It's fantastic!"

He popped the bogey into a matchbox so he could show it to his best friend, Ronnie, when he came round to play.

Peter took Ronnie straight to his room where he had hidden the matchbox.

Ronnie was just as excited as Peter. He too loved bogeys and a bogey that moved was something very special indeed.

But when Peter opened the matchbox, it was empty.

"Oh no!" cried Peter. "The bogey's escaped! My Mum will go mad if she finds it."

The two boys searched high and low. But the bogey was nowhere to be seen.

Soon it was lunch time and Ronnie had to go home.

Peter sat down at the table.

"Here we are," his Mum said, as she put two plates of cheese salad on the table. "Eat up now."

But Peter wasn't hungry. His mind was on the lost bogey. And then he saw it... It was on his mother's plate and... it was eating her lettuce.

Peter jumped up and knocked over his glass of milk.

"Never mind," said his Mum and went off to find a cloth.

As soon as her back was turned, Peter grabbed the bogey and put it in the coffee tin.

After lunch, Peter's Mum cleared the table and tidied the tin away. She put it on the very top shelf in the kitchen. Where Peter couldn't reach it.

Several days passed. Peter grew more and more worried. If his mother found the bogey, he'd be in big trouble, and no mistake. In fact, he was so worried, he even stopped picking his nose.

His Mum was delighted.

Then one day, the worst happened...

Peter's Mum had invited her friends over for coffee. She took down the coffee tin from the top shelf and opened it...

Peter's heart sank.

Then something very strange happened. Instead of finding a horrid, green bogey, a beautiful, rainbow-coloured butterfly flew out of the tin and fluttered around the kitchen.

"Isn't it beautiful," said Peter's Mum. And all her friends agreed.

"Hmm," thought Peter. "Who'd have thought that a bogey could make my Mum so happy. I wonder if there are any more."

And he set off at once to find out.

Look out for the next twelve Little Monsters!

FRIENDLY FRANCO

CLUMSY CLARISSA

BOISTEROUS BILLY

SICKLY SIMON

SERIOUS SADIE

GROWN-UP GABBY

PERFECT PRUDENCE

RUDE ROGER

DANGEROUS DAVE

CURIOUS CALVIN

DIRTY DERMOT

TANTRUM TABITHA

© SPLASH! Holdings Ltd.

Cover printed Hexachrome, inner section printed 4 colour process by Speedprint (Leeds) Ltd. Tel: 0113 245 3665.